FETCH

Published in 2015 by Hare Brand Ideas, Swannanoa, NC 28778
Written and Illustrated by Jerald Pope

ISBN: 978-0-9858787-9-5

Printed in USA
50 pages

To delve further into the artistic ouvre of Jerald Pope,
visit harebrandideas.com

FETCH

by

Jerald Pope

To Russell Presley WIlliams (2001-2013)
"A pretty good dog"

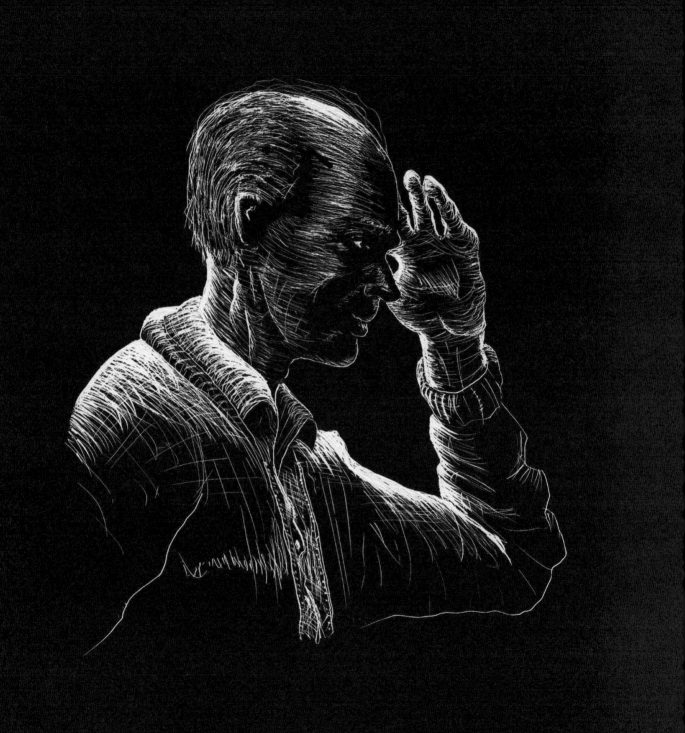

Made in the USA
Charleston, SC
23 November 2015